Say it
BOOK ONE
Act it!

10 Bible sketches

Michael Catchpool
and Pat Lunt

Kevin Mayhew

First published in 1999 by
KEVIN MAYHEW LTD
Buxhall
Stowmarket
Suffolk IP14 3DJ

0 1 2 3 4 5 6 7 8 9

ISBN 1 84003 377 0
Catalogue No 1500276

Cover design by Jonathan Stroulger
Edited by Elisabeth Bates
Typesetting by Richard Weaver
Printed in Great Britain

Contents

Acknowledgements

Thanks are due to D. Gatward Esq. for his 'jolly super' ideas and 'whizzo' encouragement!

About the Authors

Catchpool (Michael) – is not as young as he used to be. He is a Deputy-head teacher, and has a degree in Drama and Theatre Studies, as well as a cycling proficiency certificate – though he refuses to say which he is most proud of.

Lunt (Pat) is not as young as Michael used to be and has a birth certificate to prove it. He is also a teacher and works at a Junior School.

Both have a wide experience of using drama successfully in education. They have collaborated on a number of projects, performing on both commercial and local BBC radio. They are also the authors of *The Log in My Eye*, a book of 'double act sketches'.

Introduction

Q: Take one popular party game, several action-packed Bible stories and a group of willing performers and what do you get?

A: A great time had by all – with some important truths thrown in for good measure!

Are you ever in a situation where you need to explore and explain Old Testament stories or New Testament parables? Are you worried you're going to make it boring? That people aren't going to get the point? That they just won't feel involved or that it's relevant?

Well, stop worrying. *Say It – Act It!* can help. It is an invaluable drama-based resource, which will help you to help others really understand those important biblical stories and characters, together with the valuable lessons they teach us.

'But how?' you ask. 'How is it possible?'

It's easy. *Say It – Act It!* works by using as its starting point the idea behind the ever-popular party game 'Simon Says', in which one person gives instructions and the players respond. However, this simple idea has been developed so that those taking part end up performing fun, humorous and exciting stories in an enjoyable atmosphere.

How it works!

Two narrators read the exciting and entertaining scripts whilst everyone else has the fun of performing the actions described, all within the safe environment of performing with lots of other friends.

The scripts provide clear direction of actions to be performed so that no one is left unsure of what to do. The real energy comes as the performers respond to the script and the variety of actions that they are asked to do. These can range from the 'quite simple' through to the really 'quite zany'!

For *Say It – Act It!* to be most effective, all those involved need to understand the simple rules. If the narrators mention an action, such as 'They all bow to the king' then all the relevant performers do it. And the more energy they put into their performances the more fun they get out!

Each script has a cast list, so each person simply listens out for what their character is supposed to be doing. Any spoken word for the characters is done by the narrators so there is no need to worry about learning lines or indeed, saying a thing!

The scripts can be used for a wide range of group sizes. For example, if the script asks for 'servants' there can be two servants or twenty, it's up to you! The important thing is to be ready to be flexible – so even if the script calls for a 'rich man', who says you can't have a female performer?

Much of the scripts' comedy comes from the interplay between the two narrators, so they will need to be 'on their mettle' as they read. A chance to read through together beforehand can be an advantage – though not a necessity for those who really have their wits about them!

For the pieces to be really effective, the narrators need to give the participants time to perform their actions. This may involve waiting for a moment or two whilst the action unfolds. Such pauses are indicated in the scripts, where necessary, by way of an asterisk.

In the scripts the narrators sometimes call for certain actions to be repeated, as in the following example:

Narrator 1   They laughed very loudly.*

Narrator 2   Even louder than that!*

Here, the narrators are encouraging even more of the same – and then some! – adding to the humour of the situation.

So then, for the effective and entertaining re-telling of these Old and New Testament stories and parables, the narrators will need nothing more than the script provided and a helping of common sense.

And, just like the game in which it has its roots, *Say It – Act It!* really is simple!

So go on, have a go!

OLD TESTAMENT

Operation Desert Storm

otherwise known as

Wettest Summer Since Records Began – The Story of Noah

Cast   Noah
      Shem
      Ham
      Japheth
      Bad people

* Where this symbol appears in the script, the narrators wait for the appropriate action to be performed.

Narrator 1 There was once a man called Noah.

Narrator 2 Noah what?

Narrator 1 Noah good place to build a boat?

Narrator 2 *(Confused)* You what?

Narrator 1 Noah good place to build a boat? *(Explaining)* That's what he did, he built a boat. But let's start at the very beginning . . .

Narrator 2 A very good place to start.

Narrator 1 There was once a man called Noah who was very good. But everyone else was bad.

Narrator 2 They would do horrible things – like, kick the cat.*

Narrator 1 Tip the water out of the goldfish bowl.*

Narrator 2 All over their Grandma.*

Narrator 1 They'd stick their tongue out at old people.*

Narrator 2 A really long way.*

Narrator 1 And when they blew their nose, they didn't use a hankie.*

Narrator 2 They just used their sleeve.*

Narrator 1 But that's not all. They did lots of other horrible things as well.

Narrator 2 They were mean to each other. And cheated, and lied, and stole.

Narrator 1 Now God wasn't pleased with the people.

Narrator 2 So he had an idea.

Narrator 1 God would get rid of all the horrid people and all their bad ways, by washing them all away.

Narrator 2 All except Noah and his family. Who were good.

Narrator 1 So God told Noah to build a boat.

Narrator 2 A very big boat.

Narrator 1 Now Noah was surprised. He was so surprised that he began to laugh.*

Narrator 2 Very loudly.*

Narrator 1 Even louder than that.*

Narrator 2 He laughed because he lived in a desert.

Narrator 1 A desert where there was no water. But Noah was faithful.

Narrator 2 Noah knew that he would need help, so he waved to his three sons; Shem, Ham and Japheth.*

Narrator 1 Shem, Ham and Japheth waved back.*

Narrator 2   Noah was worried that Shem, Ham and Japheth had got the wrong end of the stick, so he stopped waving and simply said, 'Hurry up over here and stop messing about.'

Narrator 1   Shem, Ham and Japheth hurried over.*

Narrator 2   Conveniently carrying their heavy carpentry tools with them.*

Narrator 1   Noah explained to his sons that what they had to do was to build a big boat.

Narrator 2   Ark.

Narrator 1   What?

Narrator 2   Ark.

Narrator 1   *(Misunderstanding)* I can't hear anything.

Narrator 2   Not 'hark', Ark – They built an Ark!

Narrator 1   *(Resuming)* First they started by sawing, using big, two-handled saws.*

Narrator 2   All except Japheth, who cheated 'cos he had an electric one.*

Narrator 1   They sawed and they sawed.*

Narrator 2   Until they were sore.

Narrator 1   Their backs were sore. Their arms were sore. Their legs were sore.

Narrator 2   When Noah saw how sore they were from sawing, he saw to it that they stopped sawing and did a bit of hammering instead.

Narrator 1   With hammers and nails, they joined bits of wood together.

Narrator 2 They banged in the nails very hard.*

Narrator 1 All except Japheth, who banged his thumb very hard!*

Narrator 2 The Ark was taking shape and soon they had to paint it.

Narrator 1 They took their brushes and their paints and they started.*

Narrator 2 They slapped it here.*

Narrator 1 They slapped it there.*

Narrator 2 All except Japheth, who slapped it all over Shem.*

Narrator 1 The bad people came to laugh at Noah and his family for building a boat in the desert.*

Narrator 2 They laughed.*

Narrator 1 They jeered.*

Narrator 2 They pointed.*

Narrator 1 And pulled silly faces.*

Narrator 2 Which all made Noah and his family sad.*

Narrator 1 But they were faithful and carried on building.

Narrator 2 At last, the Ark.

Narrator 1 *(Still explaining what an ark is)* – Big boat.

Narrator 2 Whopper of a ship.

Narrator 1 Was finished!

Narrator 2 Noah, Shem, Ham and Japheth, all stood back to admire the view.*

Narrator 1   Back a bit more actually.*

Narrator 2   Just a little bit more.*

Narrator 1   Perfect. Yes, the Ark was perfect.

Narrator 2   And now came the next bit of God's plan. There were to be some special passengers.

Narrator 1   Animals! Two of each kind.

Narrator 2   Every kind. Big, small, fat, thin, clean . . . and smelly.

Narrator 1   So Noah, Shem, Ham and Japheth set about rounding up the animals.

Narrator 2   They dragged on two donkeys.*

Narrator 1   They pushed on two elephants.*

Narrator 2   They carried on two crocodiles.*

Narrator 1   Very carefully.*

Narrator 2   And between them all, they squeezed in two hippopotamuses.*

Narrator 1   *(Correcting Narrator 2, saying 'hippopot- am -I')* Hippopotami!

Narrator 2   You're a what?

Narrator 1   No, Hippopotami. Two Hippopotamuses are called Hippopotami.

Narrator 2   *(Wanting to get on)* Eventually the Ark was full. Full to the brim with different animals.

Narrator 1   Two of each kind.

Narrator 2   So Noah.

Narrator 1   And his wife.

Narrator 2   Shem.

Narrator 1   And his wife.

Narrator 2   Ham.

Narrator 1   And his wife.

Narrator 2   Japheth.

Narrator 1   And his wife.

Narrator 2   All climbed on board and shut the huge door behind them.*

Narrator 1   And locked it.*

Narrator 2   And bolted it.*

Narrator 1   And then unbolted it.*

Narrator 2   And unlocked it.*

Narrator 1   And opened the huge door again.*

Narrator 2   So Mrs Noah could leave a quick note for the milkman saying, 'No milk for the foreseeable future.

Narrator 1   Thank you.'*

Narrator 2   And then very quickly, they shut the door.*

Narrator 1   Locked it and bolted it.*

Narrator 2   Just as it began to rain.

Narrator 1   It rained and it rained and it rained.

Narrator 2   The rain came down.

Narrator 1   And the floods came up. Up and up and up.

Narrator 2 And the huge Ark began to float. It sailed away.

Narrator 1 Noah and his wife, Shem, Ham and Japheth and their wives, felt like real sailors.

Narrator 2 So much that they danced the hornpipe.*

Narrator 1 Badly!*

Narrator 2 It carried on raining. For 40 days and 40 nights.

Narrator 1 And the whole earth was covered with water.

Narrator 2 Everything was washed away.

Narrator 1 Just as God had planned.

Narrator 2 When the 40 days were up.

Narrator 1 Or down.

Narrator 2 Or over.

Narrator 1 It stopped raining. The floods went down.

Narrator 2 Not up!

Narrator 1 Down and down and down.

Narrator 2 Till at last, there was dry land again.

Narrator 1 So Noah.

Narrator 2 And his wife.

Narrator 1 Shem.

Narrator 2 And his wife.

Narrator 1 Ham.

Narrator 2 And his wife.

Narrator 1 Japheth.

Narrator 2 And his wife.

Narrator 1 Unlocked.*

Narrator 2 And unbolted the huge door.*

Narrator 1 And stepped out of the Ark.* It was a new and fresh start for the Earth.

Narrator 2 The bad had been washed away.

Narrator 1 Then God put a beautiful sign in the sky.

Narrator 2 A glorious rainbow.

Narrator 1 To show that he would never flood the Earth again.

Narrator 2 And it all happened . . .

Narrator 1 Just as God had planned!

Hola! Sprechen zie Français?

otherwise known as

Troublesome Tower –
The Story of the Tower of Babel

Cast	A whole bunch of people.

* Where this symbol appears in the script, the narrators wait for the appropriate action to be performed.

Narrator 1 A long time ago . . .

Narrator 2 A very long time ago.

Narrator 1 A very, very long time ago.

Narrator 2 There was a whole bunch of people.

Narrator 1 Crowd.

Narrator 2 What?

Narrator 1 *(Explaining)* 'Crowd'. Bananas come in bunches.

Narrator 2 *(Wishing to move on)* OK, OK. There was a whole crowd of bananas.

Narrator 1 People.

Narrator 2 A huge great bunch of a crowd of people. *(Wait for people to enter)*

Narrator 1 Who were sitting down having a chat.*

Narrator 2 About this and that.

Narrator 1 Fancy that, they were having a chat.

Narrator 2 And that was that!

Narrator 1 *(Correcting)* No it wasn't. 'Cos it wouldn't be very much of a story if it was.

Narrator 2 You're right.

Narrator 1 This crowd of people having a chat, suddenly discovered how to make bricks.*

Narrator 2 Just like that.

Narrator 1 That's enough of that.

Narrator 2 They discovered how to make bricks by baking clay in the hot sun.*

Narrator 1 The only things they baked in the hot sun before were themselves.

Narrator 2 And what wonderful tans they had.

Narrator 1 But now they had bricks.

Narrator 2 Lots and lots of lovely bricks.

Narrator 1 So they began to pile up the bricks.*

Narrator 2 *(Elaborating)* The very heavy bricks.*

Narrator 1 *(Elaborating further)* The very heavy bricks that took two people to pick them up.*

Narrator 2 When they'd piled them up, they said to themselves . . .

Narrator 1 'These bricks are super. What on earth should we do with them?'

Narrator 2 Someone suggested playing football with them.

Narrator 1 So they did.*

Narrator 2 But it hurt.*

Narrator 1   Especially when they did a header.*

Narrator 2   So they stopped.*

Narrator 1   Actually shouldn't that be footbrick, not football?

Narrator 2   I don't think it matters.

Narrator 1   After the football someone said, 'Why don't we juggle with them?'

Narrator 2   So they did.*

Narrator 1   But they kept dropping them.*

Narrator 2   On their toes.*

Narrator 1   So they stopped.*

Narrator 2   Then someone, who was rather silly said, 'Why don't we try eating them?'

Narrator 1   So they did.*

Narrator 2   But they were rather heavy on the stomach.

Narrator 1   So they stopped.*

Narrator 2   What on earth were they to do with these bricks?

Narrator 1   They thought and they thought.*

Narrator 2   And they thought and they thought.*

Narrator 1   Until one bright spark said, 'Why don't we build something?'

Narrator 2   'What an excellent idea,' they said.

Narrator 1   And everyone was so excited that they smiled.*

Narrator 2   A big, broad happy smile.*

Narrator 1   A very big, broad, happy smile.*

Narrator 2   Till one person said.

Narrator 1   'What shall we build?'

Narrator 2   So they thought and they thought.*

Narrator 1   And they thought and they thought.*

Narrator 2   Until someone said.

Narrator 1   'Why don't we build a six-tiered, triple-arched self-supporting aqueduct to allow the free-flow of fresh water from the east side of the desert to the west side, thus providing us and all our cattle with all the water we will need?'

Narrator 2   And all the people said.

Narrator 1   'Nah!'

Narrator 2   Then one smart-alec said.

Narrator 1   'Why don't we build a really tall tower to show how great we are? We'd be really famous.'

Narrator 2   'Have our picture in the paper.'

Narrator 1   'Give autographs.'

Narrator 2   'Give after-dinner speeches.'

Narrator 1   'Open supermarkets.'

Narrator 2   'It would be great.'

Narrator 1   'We'd be like gods!'

Narrator 2   And all the people said.

Narrator 1   'Brilliant!'

Narrator 2   'You bet!'

Narrator 1   'Right on!'

Narrator 2   'Gods you say? Yes please!'

Narrator 1   'That's the very thing for us!'

Narrator 2   So they set to work immediately, digging the foundations.*

Narrator 1   And then they had a tea break.*

Narrator 2   Milk.

Narrator 1   And two sugars.

Narrator 2   And then they went back to work, cementing the bricks together.*

Narrator 1   And then they had a tea break.*

Narrator 2   Milk.

Narrator 1   And three sugars.

Narrator 2   And then they were just about to start work again.

Narrator 1   But it was lunchtime.

Narrator 2   So they ate their lunch.*

Narrator 1   Sausage rolls.

Narrator 2   Very large.*

Narrator 1   Boiled eggs.

Narrator 2   Which they forgot to shell.*

Narrator 1   A plate of chilli.

Narrator 2   Very hot.*

Narrator 1 And rice pudding, which they ate with their fingers.*

Narrator 2 Because they forgot their spoons.

Narrator 1 And then they went back to work.

Narrator 2 Carefully placing brick upon brick.*

Narrator 1 Brick upon brick.*

Narrator 2 And the tower got taller and taller.

Narrator 1 So tall, they had to climb ladders.*

Narrator 2 Very tall ladders.*

Narrator 1 Which were a bit wobbly.*

Narrator 2 And which broke.*

Narrator 1 Which was a shame.

Narrator 2 Especially if you were halfway up the ladder at the time.

Narrator 1 The tower was getting taller.

Narrator 2 And the people were getting prouder.

Narrator 1 All puffed out with pride.

Narrator 2 *(Correcting)* Puffed *up* with pride.

Narrator 1 They were so puffed up with pride.

Narrator 2 They nearly burst.

Narrator 1 'Aren't we great?' they said to each other.

Narrator 2 Shaking each others' hand.*

Narrator 1 And slapping each other on the back.*

Narrator 2 'Just magnificent!'

Narrator 1 God looked down and saw the tower.

Narrator 2 And saw how proud the people had become.

Narrator 1 And he was sad.

Narrator 2 But he had an idea.

Narrator 1 To show them that they were wrong.

Narrator 2 That their big ideas would lead to trouble.

Narrator 1 So he went down and confused them all.

Narrator 2 Which wasn't difficult, because many of them were confused anyway.

Narrator 1 He confused their language.

Narrator 2 So they couldn't understand each other.

Narrator 1 They didn't have a clue what each other was going on about.

Narrator 2 Not the foggiest.

Narrator 1 When they tried to work together.

Narrator 2 It was a disaster.

Narrator 1 A shambles.

Narrator 2 A complete pig's ear.

Narrator 1 They just couldn't understand what each other was saying.

Narrator 2 And so they ended up.

Narrator 1 Dropping bricks on each other's toes.*

Narrator 2 Pouring cement down each other's shirts.*

Narrator 1   Leaving nails on chairs so that others sat on them.*

Narrator 2   Bumping into each other with their wheelbarrows.*

Narrator 1   And so the tower never got finished.

Narrator 2   Never, ever.

Narrator 1   And the very confused people.

Narrator 2   Were so confused that in their confusion they got themselves scattered.

Narrator 1   Confusingly . . . all over the place.

Narrator 2   Which meant people could never get so big for their boots again.

Narrator 1   Or come up with such a stupid idea and think that they were gods.

Narrator 2   Which they weren't.

Narrator 1   And aren't.

Narrator 2   *(Firmly)* And that's that!

Three Hundred Play Trumpet Voluntary

otherwise known as

Ever Ready with His Torch – The Story of Gideon

Cast	Gideon
	Israelites
	Midianites

* Where this symbol appears in the script, the narrators wait for the appropriate action to be performed.

Narrator 1 There was once a man.

Narrator 2 A small man.

Narrator 1 A small and very nervous man.

Narrator 2 Named Gideon.

Narrator 1 Gideon was so nervous that his knees would knock together.*

Narrator 2 Gideon was so worried that he would bite his finger nails.*

Narrator 1 Gideon was so scared that he would suck his thumb.*

Narrator 2 But God had plans for Gideon.

Narrator 1 Big plans.

Narrator 2 Big plans for a small man.

Narrator 1 *(Explaining)* The Israelites had been invaded by the Midianites.

Narrator 2 The Midianites had come stomping in.

Narrator 1 With great big steps.*

Narrator 2 *(Dramatically)* The Midianites were fierce and scary.

Narrator 1 They pulled fierce and scary faces.*

Narrator 2 And made fierce and scary noises.*

Narrator 1 And the Israelites were very scared.

Narrator 2 So scared that they covered their eyes.*

Narrator 1 And their ears.*

Narrator 2 And hoped that the Midianites would go away.

Narrator 1 But they didn't.

Narrator 2 They stayed.

Narrator 1 And did fierce and scary things.

Narrator 2 They ate all the Israelites' food.

Narrator 1 Apples.*

Narrator 2 Bananas.*

Narrator 1 Grapes.*

Narrator 2 Kentucky Fried Chicken.*

Narrator 1 *(Confessing)* Well, they didn't, but they might have done if it had been there.

Narrator 2 *(Closing the subject)* But it wasn't so they couldn't, so there.

Narrator 1 *(Resuming)* The Israelites were very unhappy.

Narrator 2 So unhappy that they began to cry.*

Narrator 1   Louder than that.*

Narrator 2   They really were very upset.

Narrator 1   What they needed was someone to save them.

Narrator 2   So they looked to the left.*

Narrator 1   They looked to the right.*

Narrator 2   They looked to the left again.*

Narrator 1   And, as nothing was coming, they walked straight across the road.*

Narrator 2   Still looking and listening as they went.*

Narrator 1   In despair, the Israelites fell to their knees.*

Narrator 2   Put their hands together.*

Narrator 1   Bowed their heads.*

Narrator 2   And prayed to God to save them.

Narrator 1   Now God had a plan.

Narrator 2   A plan to save the Israelites.

Narrator 1   A big plan, using a small man.

Narrator 2   Enter Gideon.*

Narrator 1   Gideon stood in front of the Israelites and looked sternly at them.*

Narrator 2   Even more sternly than that.*

Narrator 1   Gideon told the Israelites they needed an army.

Narrator 2   *(Confidently)* 'Your country needs you', he said.

Narrator 1   He asked for volunteers.

Narrator 2 And all the Israelites put up their hands.*

Narrator 1 And volunteered.

Narrator 2 They felt very pleased with themselves.

Narrator 1 And smiled happily at each other.*

Narrator 2 Of course, they'd put their hands down by now.*

Narrator 1 But God said a very surprising thing to Gideon.

Narrator 2 He said there were too many volunteers!

Narrator 1 Gideon was so surprised that he took a big step backwards.*

Narrator 2 And then another because he was even more surprised than that.*

Narrator 1 So Gideon told the volunteers that if anyone was scared they could go home.

Narrator 2 So the volunteers looked at each other.*

Narrator 1 And they thought.

Narrator 2 And they scratched their heads.*

Narrator 1 And then lots of them.

Narrator 2 (Informatively) Twenty-two thousand to be precise.

Narrator 1 Went home.

Narrator 2 But they did wave goodbye before they went.*

Narrator 1 God had another surprise for Gideon.

Narrator 2 'Still too many,' he said.

Narrator 1 Gideon was very surprised.

Narrator 2   So surprised that he gave a little jump in the air.*

Narrator 1   And then another because he was even more surprised than that.*

Narrator 2   But God had a way of sorting things out.

Narrator 1   Gideon led the volunteers down to a stream.

Narrator 2   They were all very thirsty and wanted a drink.

Narrator 1   Lots of them knelt down.*

Narrator 2   And began lapping up the water with their tongues.*

Narrator 1   Just like dogs.

Narrator 2   Woof. Woof.

Narrator 1   Or cats.

Narrator 2   Meow. Meow.

Narrator 1   But some drew the water up in their hands.*

Narrator 2   In a very civilised manner.*

Narrator 1   All the volunteers who had drunk like dogs.

Narrator 2   Were sent home.*

Narrator 1   *(Jovially)* With their tails between their legs.

Narrator 2   Now Gideon had his army.

Narrator 1   A very small army.

Narrator 2   *(Informatively)* Three hundred to be precise.

Narrator 1   Hardly an army at all.

Narrator 2   More like a mini-army.

Narrator 1   Or a baby army.

Narrator 2   Or an 'armyette'.

Narrator 1   Gideon and his army began to march on the spot.*

Narrator 2   Just for practice.

Narrator 1   They all turned to the right.*

Narrator 2   Then they all turned to the left.*

Narrator 1   Stood to attention.*

Narrator 2   Saluted.*

Narrator 1   Stood at ease.*

Narrator 2   And waited for Gideon to tell them what to do.

Narrator 1   'To defeat the Midianites we will need trumpets, torches and clay jars,' said Gideon.

Narrator 2   The army was so surprised that they all took a big step backwards.*

Narrator 1   And jumped in the air.*

Narrator 2   And then took another step and another jump.*

Narrator 1   Because they were more surprised than that.

Narrator 2   Each soldier got a torch.*

Narrator 1   Checked the batteries.

Narrator 2   *(To Narrator 1, disparagingly)* Not that sort of torch.

Narrator 1   And carefully put the torch in a jar.*

Narrator 2   But they weren't very careful so they all burnt their fingers.*

Narrator 1   And had to suck them very hard to make them feel better.*

Narrator 2   Then with their jar in one hand.

Narrator 1   And a trumpet in the other.

Narrator 2   And a sword in the other.

Narrator 1   *(Correcting)* Too many 'others' – that makes three hands.

Narrator 2   OK . . . a sword at their waist.

Narrator 1   They set off for the Midianite camp.

Narrator 2   They went very quietly.

Narrator 1   Walking on tip-toe.*

Narrator 2   It was very dark.

Narrator 1   So dark, they kept bumping into each other.*

Narrator 2   At last they arrived.

Narrator 1   And stood very still.*

Narrator 2   As still as statues.*

Narrator 1   Nobody moved.

Narrator 2   Nobody dared to breathe.

Narrator 1   *(Disbelieving)* What?

Narrator 2   Oh, OK then, they were allowed to breathe but they did it very quietly.*

Narrator 1   Suddenly Gideon gave the signal.

Narrator 2   He raised both hands in the air.*

Narrator 1 And waved them about.*

Narrator 2 But because it was so dark, no one saw him.

Narrator 1 So Gideon clapped his hands three times.*

Narrator 2 *(With building drama)* The soldiers threw the jars onto the floor.*

Narrator 1 The jars smashed.

Narrator 2 And the torches shone brightly in the night.

Narrator 1 The soldiers put the trumpets to their lips and blew.*

Narrator 2 And then they blew again.*

Narrator 1 And again, just to make sure.*

Narrator 2 And they shouted.*

Narrator 1 'A sword for the Lord and for Gideon.'

Narrator 2 The Midianites.

Narrator 1 *(Reminding)* The fierce and scary Midianites.

Narrator 2 Were so startled.

Narrator 1 By the bright lights and the noise.

Narrator 2 That they ran away.*

Narrator 1 They fled.*

Narrator 2 They chickened out.

Narrator 1 They disappeared in complete disarray.

Narrator 2 They had been defeated.

Narrator 1 *(Summing up)* So a small man.

Narrator 2 With a very small army.

Narrator 1 Who relied on God.

Narrator 2 Had a very big victory!

Head off at the Pass

otherwise known as

The Bigger They Come, the Harder They Fall – The Story of David and Goliath

Cast   David
                Goliath
                Saul
                Israelites
                Philistines

* Where this symbol appears in the script, the narrators wait for the appropriate action to be performed.

Narrator 1   There was once a boy named David.

Narrator 2   Who was a shepherd.

Narrator 1   He looked after sheep.

Narrator 2   That's why he was a shepherd, and not a goatherd.

Narrator 1   Who looks after goats.

Narrator 2   *(To Narrator 1)* So who looks after elephants?

Narrator 1   *(Ignoring the question)* There was once a shepherd boy called David.

Narrator 2   And that is where we must leave him.

Narrator 1   For now.

Narrator 2   Quietly tending his sheep.

Narrator 1   For on the other side of the hills, two armies were preparing for war.

Narrator 2   There was the Israelite army.

Narrator 1 The soldiers were getting ready.

Narrator 2 Sharpening their swords.*

Narrator 1 Very carefully so as not to cut themselves.*

Narrator 2 Oiling their armour.*

Narrator 1 And polishing their boots.*

Narrator 2 And then polishing them a bit more after the commanding officer had said what a bad job they'd done the first time.

Narrator 1 And then they practised their sword skills.

Narrator 2 The noble art.

Narrator 1 The parry.*

Narrator 2 The thrust.*

Narrator 1 The chopping the head off.*

Narrator 2 Not that far away the Philistine army was preparing for war.

Narrator 1 Their soldiers were getting ready.

Narrator 2 Sharpening their spears.*

Narrator 1 Cleaning off their shields.*

Narrator 2 Polishing their armour.*

Narrator 1 And doing the washing up from the day before.*

Narrator 2 Because they'd been too busy preparing for war to do it then.

Narrator 1 The Philistine soldiers were very confident.

Narrator 2 And struck confident poses.*

Narrator 1   And had smug expressions on their faces.*

Narrator 2   Very smug.*

Narrator 1   *(Rather mysteriously)* They were confident because they had a secret weapon.

Narrator 2   Except of course, it wasn't very secret, because everyone could see it for miles around.

Narrator 1   'It'? Don't you mean 'him'?

Narrator 2   Yes 'him'. Their secret weapon was a 'him'.

Narrator 1   A very big 'him'.

Narrator 2   A very big 'him' indeed.

Narrator 1   A giant 'him' in fact.

Narrator 2   In fact, a giant!

Narrator 1   A giant named Goliath.

Narrator 2   Goliath was enormous!

Narrator 1   He was nine feet tall.

Narrator 2   With huge bulging muscles.

Narrator 1   Even his muscles had muscles.

Narrator 2   And he was very scary.

Narrator 1   He was so scary, even the Philistines were scared of him.

Narrator 2   Whenever they saw him their knees would knock.*

Narrator 1   Their teeth would chatter.*

Narrator 2   And they would wobble like nervous jellies.*

Narrator 1 And if that's how the Philistines felt, just think about the poor Israelites!

Narrator 2 When they saw Goliath, they were terrified.

Narrator 1 Petrified!

Narrator 2 Scared out of their wits.

Narrator 1 And a little bit anxious as well.

Narrator 2 They were so scared that the Israelite soldiers began to cry.*

Narrator 1 And sob.*

Narrator 2 And suck their thumbs.*

Narrator 1 And ask for their mummy.*

Narrator 2 But their mummy was busy so she couldn't come.

Narrator 1 Every morning Goliath would march up and down and challenge the Israelite army.

Narrator 2 'Send your best soldier up here and we shall fight!'

Narrator 1 He would say.

Narrator 2 And every morning, the Israelite soldiers would get in a little huddle to see if anybody wanted to go and fight.*

Narrator 1 But nobody did.

Narrator 2 Everyone had an excuse.

Narrator 1 They all suddenly had very bad backs.*

Narrator 2 And painful toes.*

Narrator 1 And splitting headaches.*

Narrator 2   And terrible colds.*

Narrator 1   And notes from their mum.*

Narrator 2   No one would take up the challenge.

Narrator 1   This went on for forty days.

Narrator 2   Until, suddenly there was a shepherd boy called David.

Narrator 1   What, the one we met before?

Narrator 2   The very same.

Narrator 1   David was a brave shepherd.

Narrator 2   Who had fought lions and bears to protect his sheep.

Narrator 1   He wasn't scared of Goliath.

Narrator 2   Even though Goliath was bigger than a lion.

Narrator 1   And bigger than a bear.

Narrator 2   No! He wasn't scared because he knew God was on his side.

Narrator 1   David went up to the king.

Narrator 2   Whose name happened to be Saul.

Narrator 1   And bowed very low.*

Narrator 2   Saul looked carefully at David.*

Narrator 1   And then he looked again.*

Narrator 2   And then he looked across at Goliath.*

Narrator 1   He wasn't sure it was such a good idea.

Narrator 2   But David was adamant.

Narrator 1   *(To Narrator 2)* I thought you said he was a shepherd.

Narrator 2   He was that as well. But he was determined to fight Goliath.

Narrator 1   Because he knew that God would be with him.

Narrator 2   Saul called his soldiers to bring his royal armour to David.

Narrator 1   They helped him put it on.

Narrator 2   First the breastplate.*

Narrator 1   So heavy it took two people to carry it.*

Narrator 2   Then the helmet.*

Narrator 1   So heavy it took three people to carry it.*

Narrator 2   Well, Saul did have a bit of a big head.

Narrator 1   Then the sword and shield.*

Narrator 2   Which were so heavy they took six people to carry them.*

Narrator 1   David just stood there.

Narrator 2   And stood there.

Narrator 1   And stood there.

Narrator 2   That's all he did. He just stood there.

Narrator 1   He didn't do anything else.

Narrator 2   He couldn't! The armour was so heavy that he couldn't move.

Narrator 1   Not a muscle.

Narrator 2   'I don't need all this!' said David. 'God will be with me.'

Narrator 1   So the soldiers took all the armour away.

Narrator 2   The very heavy sword and shield.*

Narrator 1   The very heavy helmet.*

Narrator 2   And the very heavy breastplate.*

Narrator 1   And David set off to fight Goliath.

Narrator 2   With a simple sling in his hand.

Narrator 1   The Israelite soldiers were very impressed.

Narrator 2   And they smiled.*

Narrator 1   And they clapped.*

Narrator 2   And they cheered.*

Narrator 1   Particularly as it was David going to meet Goliath and not them.

Narrator 2   When Goliath and the Philistine army saw David.

Narrator 1   They laughed.*

Narrator 2   And they laughed.*

Narrator 1   And they laughed.*

Narrator 2   They laughed so much they could hardly stand up.

Narrator 1   'Is this your champion?' Goliath jeered.

Narrator 2   But David said, 'Today God will deliver you into my hand!'

Narrator 1 'Nonsense!' I come against you with my huge spear.

Narrator 2 And David said, 'I come against you in the name of the Lord!'

Narrator 1 'And soon everyone will know the power of the God of Israel.'

Narrator 2 'A likely story!' said Goliath.

Narrator 1 Who was a little bit proud to say the least.

Narrator 2 But then you know what they say?

Narrator 1 About pride coming before certain things.

Narrator 2 Such as falls.

Narrator 1 Goliath picked up his mighty spear.*

Narrator 2 David picked up a tiny pebble.*

Narrator 1 Goliath shook his spear in his hand.*

Narrator 2 David put his pebble in his sling.*

Narrator 1 Goliath swung his spear in the air.*

Narrator 2 David swung his sling round and round.*

Narrator 1 And round and round.*

Narrator 2 And then he shot.*

Narrator 1 And the pebble shot straight at Goliath's head.

Narrator 2 Crack!

Narrator 1 Bam!

Narrator 2 Kapow!

Narrator 1 Bingo! Right between the eyes.

Narrator 2   Goliath fell to the ground.*

Narrator 1   And David walked over and cut off Goliath's head.*

Narrator 2   With Goliath's own sword.

Narrator 1   Which was ironic.

Narrator 2   The Philistine army couldn't believe it.

Narrator 1   They gasped in amazement.*

Narrator 2   Very big gasps.*

Narrator 1   'Cos they were very amazed.

Narrator 2   Their secret weapon was no more.

Narrator 1   They shook their heads in disappointment.*

Narrator 2   The Israelite army was ecstatic.

Narrator 1   They clapped.*

Narrator 2   And they cheered.*

Narrator 1   And they danced.*

Narrator 2   'Cos the Philistine secret weapon was no more.

Narrator 1   David had beaten Goliath.

Narrator 2   Because David had put his trust in.

Narrator 1   A sling.

Narrator 2   A pebble.

Narrator 1   And the mighty God of Israel!

Friends Feared Fried in Fiery Furnace!

otherwise known as

In the Heat of the Moment – The Story of Shadrach, Meshach and Abednego

Cast
Shadrach
Meshach
Abednego
King Nebuchadnezzar
Musicians
Soldiers
Variety of other court officials

* Where this symbol appears in the script, the narrators wait for the appropriate action to be performed.

Narrator 1   Long ago King Nebuchadnezzar built a statue.

Narrator 2   A very big statue.

Narrator 1   With ninety feet.

Narrator 2   *(Correcting)* No, no . . . ninety feet high.

Narrator 1   *(Wanting to press on)* Nebuchadnezzar was very pleased with the statue.

Narrator 2   Very pleased indeed.

Narrator 1   He was so pleased he wanted everyone to see it.

Narrator 2   So he called for the governors from the east.*

Narrator 1   And the governors from the west.*

Narrator 2   And the governors from the north.*

Narrator 1   And the governors from the south.*

Narrator 2   And the councillors from over here.*

Narrator 1   And the councillors from over there.*

Narrator 2   And the magistrates from the left.*

Narrator 1   And the magistrates from the right.*

Narrator 2   And the advisors.*

Narrator 1   And the treasurers.*

Narrator 2   And the judges.*

Narrator 1   And the officials.*

Narrator 2   Who all came together.

Narrator 1   'Cos it was cheaper to share the same camel.

Narrator 2   Everybody bowed to King Nebuchadnezzar.*

Narrator 1   But he didn't bow back.

Narrator 2   Because he was the king.

Narrator 1   Nebuchadnezzar showed them the statue.*

Narrator 2   With its ninety feet.

Narrator 1   Which *was* ninety feet.

Narrator 2   The governors were impressed.*

Narrator 1   East, west, north and south.

Narrator 2   The councillors were impressed.*

Narrator 1   From over here and over there.

Narrator 2   The magistrates were impressed.*

Narrator 1   Both on the left and on the right.

Narrator 2   The advisors, the treasurers, the judges and the officials were all impressed together.*

Narrator 1   'Cos it saved money.

Narrator 2   Everyone was so impressed they gasped in wonder.*

Narrator 1   They pointed and they stared.*

Narrator 2   They stared and they pointed.*

Narrator 1   At the fantastic statue.

Narrator 2   'Now,' said Nebuchadnezzar.

Narrator 1   And here's the important bit.

Narrator 2   'Everyone must bow down and worship this statue.

Narrator 1   When they hear the musicians play.'

Narrator 2   Pipes.*

Narrator 1   Harps.*

Narrator 2   Lyre.*

Narrator 1   *(Pretending to misunderstand)* No, it's true.

Narrator 2   *(Ignoring last comment)* Trumpets.*

Narrator 1   Comb and paper.*

Narrator 2   *(Gently accusing)* Liar.

Narrator 1   *(Confessing)* Oh, alright, drums then.*

Narrator 2   *(Grandly)* 'Oh yes,'

Narrator 1   Said Nebuchadnezzar.

Narrator 2   'One last thing.

Narrator 1   If you don't bow down when the music starts.

Narrator 2   *(Suggesting a possible answer)* You're out and you don't get a balloon?

Narrator 1   No, you get burnt to death in a huge fiery furnace.'

Narrator 2   The musicians began to play.

Narrator 1   Pipes.*

Narrator 2   Harps.*

Narrator 1   Lyre.*

Narrator 2   *(Again pretending to misunderstand)* No, it's true.

Narrator 1   *(Ignoring last comment)* Trumpets.*

Narrator 2   As soon as they heard the music.

Narrator 1   The governors.

Narrator 2   And the councillors.

Narrator 1   And the magistrates.

Narrator 2   And the advisors.

Narrator 1   And the treasurers.

Narrator 2   And the judges.

Narrator 1   And the officials.

Narrator 2   All bowed down and worshipped the statue.*

Narrator 1   Which was no surprise.

Narrator 2   'Cos no one fancied being barbecued.

Narrator 1   Now, some astrologers came to Nebuchadnezzar with some news.

Narrator 2   They bowed to Nebuchadnezzar and said.*

Narrator 1   'When the music plays.

Narrator 2   The pipes.

Narrator 1   The harps.

Narrator 2   Lyre.

Narrator 1   *(Takes deep breath as if to say the familiar response 'No, it's true.')*

Narrator 2   *(Rounding on Narrator 1)* Don't even think about it.

Narrator 1   But I wasn't . . .

Narrator 2   *(Cutting over Narrator 1)* Everybody bows down and worships the statue.

Narrator 1   Except for three people.

Narrator 2   Shadrach.

Narrator 1   *(Excitedly)* Hooray!

Narrator 2   Meshach.

Narrator 1   Hooray!

Narrator 2   And Abednego.'

Narrator 1   Hooray!

Narrator 2   Nebuchadnezzar was furious.

Narrator 1   He jumped up and down in rage.*

Narrator 2   He stamped his feet in anger.*

Narrator 1   He beat his chest in fury.*

Narrator 2   And demanded that Shadrach, Meshach and Abednego.

Narrator 1   Were brought to him at once.

Narrator 2   *(Matter of fact)* Which they were.

Narrator 1   By some soldiers.*

Narrator 2   Who pushed them towards the king roughly.*

Narrator 1   Nebuchadnezzar called for the musicians to play.*

Narrator 2   The pipes.*

Narrator 1   The harps.*

Narrator 2   The thing that is quite small and looks a bit like a harp.*

Narrator 1   *(Suggesting)* Lyre?

Narrator 2   No, it's true.

Narrator 1   And trumpets.*

Narrator 2   Everyone bowed down to the statue.*

Narrator 1   Absolutely everyone.*

Narrator 2   Except Shadrach, Meshach and Abednego.

Narrator 1   They just stood there.*

Narrator 2   Looking at King Nebuchadnezzar with their hands in their pockets.*

Narrator 1   And then they said.

Narrator 2   'We will not bow down to the statue.'

Narrator 1   'Then you'll be thrown in the fiery furnace!' said Nebuchadnezzar.

Narrator 2 'Our God is able to save us from fire.' said Shadrach, Meshach and Abednego.

Narrator 1 'And even if he doesn't, we will not bow down and worship that statue instead of him.'

Narrator 2 'So there!'

Narrator 1 Nebuchadnezzar was furious. Even more furious than when he'd been furious before.

Narrator 2 And he was very furious then.

Narrator 1 So you can imagine how furious he was now.

Narrator 2 He was so furious.

Narrator 1 That he shook with rage.*

Narrator 2 Shook like a huge royal jelly.*

Narrator 1 And then he ordered a huge fiery furnace to be built.

Narrator 2 Everybody rushed around building the furnace.*

Narrator 1 First they put on small pieces of kindling wood.*

Narrator 2 Then slightly bigger sticks.*

Narrator 1 Then they put on branches.*

Narrator 2 Then they put on logs.*

Narrator 1 Then they got really carried away.

Narrator 2 And carried on huge trees.*

Narrator 1 Which took lots of them to carry.*

Narrator 2 Because they were very heavy.

Narrator 1 And then just to make sure it would burn really well.

Narrator 2   They covered the whole thing in petrol.*

Narrator 1   Well, they would have done but they didn't have any petrol.

Narrator 2   And no one knew what it was anyway.

Narrator 1   So they didn't bother.

Narrator 2   They lit the furnace.*

Narrator 1   And the flames shot into the air.

Narrator 2   It was so hot that all the people took a step back.*

Narrator 1   And then another step back.*

Narrator 2   Because it was hotter than they realised.

Narrator 1   But Nebuchadnezzar said.

Narrator 2   'Make it seven times hotter!'

Narrator 1   So they gathered more sticks.*

Narrator 2   And branches.*

Narrator 1   And logs.*

Narrator 2   And trees.*

Narrator 1   And piled them onto the fire.*

Narrator 2   And all the people crouched down.*

Narrator 1   And blew at the fire.*

Narrator 2   To make it even hotter.

Narrator 1   The flames leapt even higher into the air.

Narrator 2   And singed off everybody's eyebrows.

Narrator 1   Nebuchadnezzar ordered Shadrach, Meshach and Abednego to be thrown into the fiery furnace.

Narrator 2   Some strong soldiers.

Narrator 1   Very strong soldiers.

Narrator 2   Stood to attention.*

Narrator 1   Saluted.*

Narrator 2   And then tied up Shadrach, Meshach and Abednego.*

Narrator 1   Very tightly.*

Narrator 2   Then they were pushed into the fiery furnace.*

Narrator 1   Everybody peered into the flames.*

Narrator 2   The fire was so hot, people shielded their faces with their hands.*

Narrator 1   And screwed their eyes up.*

Narrator 2   In the fire, to everyone's amazement.

Narrator 1   They saw four figures.

Narrator 2   Nebuchadnezzar's mouth dropped open.*

Narrator 1   So did everybody else's.*

Narrator 2   Nebuchadnezzar pointed at the four figures.*

Narrator 1   So did everybody else.*

Narrator 2   'Look!' he said. 'We threw three men into the fire.'

Narrator 1   'But I can see four!'

Narrator 2   'And the fourth looks like a god!'

Narrator 1   Nebuchadnezzar bowed his head.*

Narrator 2   So did everyone else.*

Narrator 1   He called for Shadrach, Meshach and Abednego to come out of the fire.

Narrator 2   And they did.*

Narrator 1   Everyone stepped back in amazement.*

Narrator 2   Further than that – they were much more amazed.*

Narrator 1   Shadrach, Meshach and Abednego were completely unharmed.

Narrator 2   They weren't singed or burnt.

Narrator 1   Or fried or roasted.

Narrator 2   Not one hair on their head was damaged.

Narrator 1   They didn't even smell of smoke.

Narrator 2   Nebuchadnezzar fell to his knees.*

Narrator 1   So did everyone else.*

Narrator 2   'The God of Shadrach, Meshach and Abednego is a great God!' said Nebuchadnezzar.

Narrator 1   'No one must say a word against their God.'

Narrator 2   'For he is a great God indeed.'

Narrator 1   And Nebuchadnezzar knew this to be true.

Narrator 2   *(With feeling)* And so did everybody else!

NEW TESTAMENT

Waterside Property Plummets

otherwise known as

The Parable of the Wise and Foolish Builders

Cast   Wise Man
            Foolish Man
            Builders for the wise man
            Builders for the foolish man

* Where this symbol appears in the script, the narrators wait for the appropriate action to be performed.

Narrator 1   There were once two men.

Narrator 2   One wise.

Narrator 1   And one foolish.

Narrator 2   Who both had an idea.

Narrator 1   An idea of building a house.

Narrator 2   For themselves.

Narrator 1   So the wise man set off to look for a place to build.

Narrator 2   And so did the foolish man.

Narrator 1   They looked up high.*

Narrator 2   They looked down low.*

Narrator 1   They looked behind them.*

Narrator 2   And in front of them.*

Narrator 1   To the left.*

Narrator 2   And to the right.*

Narrator 1   Until there were no other directions they could look.

Narrator 2   At last, they found the very spot they would use.

Narrator 1   'Bingo!' they said.

Narrator 2   Except they didn't, 'cos no-one had heard of bingo.

Narrator 1   Let alone played it.

Narrator 2   So they just said, 'Here's the very spot!'

Narrator 1   And pointed at it.*

Narrator 2   *(To Narrator 1)* Not the same spot.

Narrator 1   What?

Narrator 2   The spot.

Narrator 1   What spot?

Narrator 2   The spot they'd found was not the same spot as each other.

Narrator 1   No, the wise man had found a spot on a rock.

Narrator 2   The foolish man had found a spot on the end of his nose.

Narrator 1   Which he tried to squeeze.*

Narrator 2   Which only made it worse.

Narrator 1   So he stopped and pointed to the spot he'd found on some sand.*

Narrator 2   They were both ready to start.

Narrator 1   So the wise man called in some builders.

Narrator 2   And so did the foolish man.

Narrator 1   The builders came carrying their heavy tools.*

Narrator 2   Their very heavy tools.*

Narrator 1   They put the tools down.*

Narrator 2   On the foolish man's foot.

Narrator 1   By mistake.

Narrator 2   Which made him hop about.*

Narrator 1   Then they looked carefully at the spots.*

Narrator 2   *(To Narrator 1)* On the nose?

Narrator 1   No, on the ground.

Narrator 2   They walked up and down on the spot on the rock.*

Narrator 1   They jumped up and down on the spot on the rock.*

Narrator 2   They stamped very hard on the spot on the rock.*

Narrator 1   Then they nodded their heads.*

Narrator 2   They all agreed.

Narrator 1   It was rock all right.

Narrator 2   Then they walked up and down on the spot on the sand.*

Narrator 1   They jumped up and down on the spot on the sand.*

Narrator 2   They made sandcastles on the spot on the sand.*

Narrator 1   Then they nodded.*

Narrator 2   They all agreed.

Narrator 1   It was sand all right.

Narrator 2   The foolish man turned to the builders and told them.

Narrator 1   He wanted his house built as quickly as they could.*

Narrator 2   The builders shook their heads and tutted.*

Narrator 1   As only builders can.

Narrator 2   They pointed to the spot on the sand.*

Narrator 1   And began to laugh.*

Narrator 2   Very loudly.*

Narrator 1   'You can't build a house here, there's no firm foundation.'

Narrator 2   And they wagged their fingers at him.*

Narrator 1   To show that they meant it.

Narrator 2   But the foolish man wouldn't listen.

Narrator 1   And covered his ears with his hands.*

Narrator 2   'I want a house and I want it quick,' he said.

Narrator 1   'So build me a house right here!'

Narrator 2   So the builders set to work.*

Narrator 1   Whilst the wise man looked through some interior decor magazines.*

Narrator 2   For a few ideas on colour washes and delightful effects achievable with a natural sponge and a bit of imagination.

Narrator 1   The builders got out their shovels and began digging.*

Narrator 2   And digging.*

Narrator 1   And then they wheeled things away in wheelbarrows.*

Narrator 2   Very wobbly wheelbarrows.*

Narrator 1   Of course, the foolish man helped too.*

Narrator 2   He was anxious for his house to be built.

Narrator 1   Then they got the bricks ready.

Narrator 2   To start building.*

Narrator 1   And then . . . they had a tea break.

Narrator 2   With a cup of tea and a slice of cake.*

Narrator 1   Very sticky cake.*

Narrator 2   With very chewy bits in.*

Narrator 1   And then they set to work.

Narrator 2   Building the house.*

Narrator 1   Of course, the foolish man helped too.*

Narrator 2   He was anxious to get his house finished.

Narrator 1   Because the house had no real foundation it was soon finished.

Narrator 2   And the foolish man gave the builders a cheery wave.*

Narrator 1   And a cheque.*

Narrator 2   And moved in, closing the door behind him.*

Narrator 1 Now the builders went to see the wise man.

Narrator 2 Ready to build his house.

Narrator 1 On the rock.

Narrator 2 They began digging.*

Narrator 1 And digging.*

Narrator 2 It was hot and tiring work.

Narrator 1 They used shovels.*

Narrator 2 And pick-axes.*

Narrator 1 And just wished that someone would hurry up and invent the pneumatic drill.

Narrator 2 The rock was so solid.

Narrator 1 Of course, the wise man joined in.*

Narrator 2 He was anxious to make sure his house was built properly.

Narrator 1 They dug and they dug.*

Narrator 2 And they wheeled things away in wheelbarrows.*

Narrator 1 Still with wobbly wheels.*

Narrator 2 At last they were ready to begin building.

Narrator 1 So they had a tea break.*

Narrator 2 With a cup of tea and a doughnut.*

Narrator 1 A jam doughnut.*

Narrator 2 A jam doughnut so full of jam that it squirted out all down their shirts.*

Narrator 1 At last they began to build.

Narrator 2 The walls on the solid foundation of the rock.

Narrator 1 Of course, the wise man joined in.*

Narrator 2 He was anxious to make sure that his house was built properly.

Narrator 1 They built and they built.*

Narrator 2 Until at last.

Narrator 1 The house was finished.

Narrator 2 The wise man gave the builders a cheery wave.*

Narrator 1 But no cheque.

Narrator 2 Because he had wisely chosen to pay by regular easily-managed monthly payments.

Narrator 1 With 0 per cent finance for the first three years.

Narrator 2 Then he went in to his house.*

Narrator 1 Closing the door behind him.*

Narrator 2 And it was a good job that he did.

Narrator 1 For no sooner was the door shut.

Narrator 2 Than the rain began to fall.

Narrator 1 Very, very hard.

Narrator 2 The wise man and the foolish man peered out of their windows at the rain.*

Narrator 1 And shook their heads.*

Narrator 2 Typical summer weather, they thought.

Narrator 1 The wind began to blow.

Narrator 2 Very, very hard.

Narrator 1 And the foolish man began to shake.*

Narrator 2 Because his house was shaking.

Narrator 1 The foolish man began to sway from side to side.*

Narrator 2 Because his house was swaying from side to side.

Narrator 1 The wise man, meanwhile, stood perfectly still.*

Narrator 2 Because his house was perfectly still.

Narrator 1 The foolish man began to wibble and wobble.*

Narrator 2 Because his house was wibbling and wobbling.

Narrator 1 The foolish man fell with a crash to the floor.*

Narrator 2 Because his house had just fallen with a crash to the floor.

Narrator 1 Because all the wind and the rain had knocked it down.

Narrator 2 Because it had no foundations.

Narrator 1 The wise man sat down and had a cup of tea, safe and secure.*

Narrator 2 Because his house was safe and secure.

Narrator 1 Because it had firm foundations.

Narrator 2 He had built on something solid.

Narrator 1 Solid as a rock.

Narrator 2 Rock solid!

Debt Worries? – Easy Terms Available

otherwise known as

The Parable of the Unforgiving Servant

Cast   King
Servants
Harold (an unforgiving fellow)
Bob (an unfortunate debtor to Harold)

* Where this symbol appears in the script, the narrators wait for the appropriate action to be performed.

Narrator 1   There was once a king who was at a loose end.

Narrator 2   And so he tried to tie it up.

Narrator 1   *(To Narrator 2)* What?

Narrator 2   *(To Narrator 1)* The loose end.

Narrator 1   *(To Narrator 2)* No he didn't, it wasn't that sort of loose end.

Narrator 2   *(To Narrator 1)* I see.

Narrator 1   Let's start again. There was once a king who was at a loose end.

Narrator 2   So he called in his servants to ask them what he ought to do.*

Narrator 1   The servants came in and bowed low to the king.*

Narrator 2   And then they bowed again.*

Narrator 1   Because they were rather creepy servants.

Narrator 2   Who were hoping for a pay rise.

Narrator 1 The king explained that he was at a loose end and asked for suggestions of what to do.

Narrator 2 'How about tennis?' said the servants and gave a quick demonstration.*

Narrator 1 'Or juggling?' they said, and showed the king exactly what they meant.*

Narrator 2 Or what about a game of 'Twister'?

Narrator 1 The king wasn't sure what 'Twister' was so the servants showed him.*

Narrator 2 Not surprisingly, the king was not that impressed.

Narrator 1 Until one servant suggested that the king could settle his accounts.

Narrator 2 The king was delighted and smiled a big, broad smile.*

Narrator 1 A very big, broad smile.*

Narrator 2 And called for the servants to bring in his books of accounts.

Narrator 1 The servants brought in the books of accounts.*

Narrator 2 The very heavy books of accounts.*

Narrator 1 Which were in fact so heavy that they had to be brought in in wheelbarrows.*

Narrator 2 The king began to look through the books, peering carefully at all the columns of figures.*

Narrator 1 Till at last he found something so interesting that he gave a little jump.*

Narrator 2 In fact, it was so interesting he gave another jump, just for good measure.*

Narrator 1   'There is someone here, called Harold, who owes me millions and millions of pounds.'

Narrator 2   Said the king, not being one for exaggeration.

Narrator 1   The king ordered that Harold be brought to him at once.

Narrator 2   So the servants marched off to find Harold.*

Narrator 1   They found him and dragged him.*

Narrator 2   Gently, so as not to hurt him too much.*

Narrator 1   Back to the king.

Narrator 2   Which was all rather embarrassing because Harold had been in the bath at the time.

Narrator 1   And only had time to grab his dressing gown.

Narrator 2   When Harold saw the king he fell to his knees.*

Narrator 1   And then he did it again, just to make sure the king was really impressed.*

Narrator 2   'Whatever do you want, your majesty?' asked Harold.

Narrator 1   'I want my money,' said the king.

Narrator 2   And all the servants nodded in agreement.*

Narrator 1   And wagged their fingers at Harold.*

Narrator 2   'How much do I owe?' asked Harold.

Narrator 1   'Millions and millions,' said the king, looking very stern.*

Narrator 2   All the other servants looked very stern as well.*

Narrator 1   In fact, they all tried to look sterner than each other to show they were in agreement with the king.*

Narrator 2   Poor old Harold took his wallet out of his pocket.*

Narrator 1   And carefully looked inside.*

Narrator 2   'I don't have millions and millions,' he said.

Narrator 1   And he showed the king what was in his wallet.*

Narrator 2   A shopping list.*

Narrator 1   A rather bent photo of his wife and kids.*

Narrator 2   A bit of fluff.*

Narrator 1   And a toenail clipping.*

Narrator 2   The king was not impressed and shook his head.*

Narrator 1   His own head, that is – not Harold's.*

Narrator 2   All the servants shook their heads as well.*

Narrator 1   'Then,' said the king, 'if you cannot repay your debt.'

Narrator 2   'You will be thrown into jail!'

Narrator 1   'And your wife and kids – nice photo by the way – will be sold as slaves!'

Narrator 2   Harold began to cry.*

Narrator 1   To sob.*

Narrator 2   To weep.*

Narrator 1   To blub.*

Narrator 2   It was so moving that all the servants began to cry.*

Narrator 1   And sob.*

Narrator 2   And weep.*

Narrator 1   And blub.*

Narrator 2   Even the king began to cry and sob and weep and blub.*

Narrator 1   Till at last, as he wiped his tears away with a hankie.*

Narrator 2   The king said, 'Your debt will be cancelled. You have nothing to fear. You may return to your family.'

Narrator 1   Harold was so overjoyed that he leapt in the air.*

Narrator 2   And then went to hug the king.*

Narrator 1   But quickly thought better of it.

Narrator 2   And shook his hand instead.*

Narrator 1   All the other servants were so happy that they smiled big, happy smiles.*

Narrator 2   And waved to Harold as he left. And then secretly followed him out.*

Narrator 1   On his way out, Harold met another man.*

Narrator 2   And this man owed him some money.

Narrator 1   50p!

Narrator 2   As much as that?!

Narrator 1   Oh yes.

Narrator 2   'You owe me 50p,' said Harold.

Narrator 1   The other man.

Narrator 2   Whom we shall call Bob, to avoid confusion.

Narrator 1   Was so surprised that he took a step back.*

Narrator 2   And then another.*

Narrator 1   'Well,' said Harold to Bob. 'I'm waiting.'

Narrator 2   Bob reached into his pocket to pull out his wallet.*

Narrator 1   And pulled out an old hankie.*

Narrator 2   A piece of string.*

Narrator 1   Some half-chewed chewing gum.*

Narrator 2   And at last, his wallet.*

Narrator 1   Bob peered inside and then shook his head.*

Narrator 2   'I'm afraid I don't have 50p,' he said.

Narrator 1   Harold scowled angrily at Bob.*

Narrator 2   Very angrily.*

Narrator 1   And shook his fist at him.*

Narrator 2   'You are in debt to me and you cannot pay . . . then you will have to pay!'

Narrator 1   He said.

Narrator 2   'But I can't pay!' said Bob.

Narrator 1   'That is why you will have to pay,' said Harold.

Narrator 2   'You will have to pay for not being able to pay.'

Narrator 1   Ooh, I say.

Narrator 2   'You will go to prison and your family will be sold as slaves,' Harold said, pointing at Bob.*

Narrator 1   The other servants, who had been secretly watching all of this, hurried back to the king.

Narrator 2   They all bowed low.*

Narrator 1   And then bowed low again.*

Narrator 2   'Cos they had their minds on their Christmas bonus.

Narrator 1   They told the king all about how Harold had treated Bob.

Narrator 2   The king was horrified and stood with his hands on his hips to show how indignant he felt.*

Narrator 1   All the servants stood with their hands on their hips.*

Narrator 2   Because they thought that was what the king would want them to do.

Narrator 1   The king ordered them to go and fetch Harold.

Narrator 2   The servants went out, found him and brought him back.*

Narrator 1   He fell to his knees in front of the king.*

Narrator 2   But the king was not impressed.

Narrator 1   'I have forgiven you much, but you were not able to forgive someone else just a tiny amount.'

Narrator 2   'You really will be thrown into jail this time. And your family sold as slaves.'

Narrator 1   'And it's no good blubbing. 'Cos it won't wash!'

Narrator 2   All the other servants nodded in agreement.*

Narrator 1   And thought how foolish Harold had been.

72

Narrator 2   Not to realise just how lucky he had been.

Narrator 1   When his huge debt had been cancelled.

Narrator 2   By the generous king!

Ask and It Shall Be Given

otherwise known as

The Parable of the Persistent Friend

Cast | Man
His wife
His children
Friend (persistent)

* Where this symbol appears in the script, the narrators wait for the appropriate action to be performed.

Narrator 1   There was once a man.

Narrator 2   And his wife.

Narrator 1   And their children.

Narrator 2   Who were just finishing their evening meal.

Narrator 1   It was such a nice evening meal.

Narrator 2   That they all licked their plates clean.*

Narrator 1   Which was rather bad manners.

Narrator 2   But saved on the washing up.

Narrator 1   Then, because it was evening, the whole family went to the door.*

Narrator 2   And bolted it.*

Narrator 1   And locked it.*

Narrator 2   Well, they would have locked it but they couldn't find the key.

Narrator 1   So the whole family started searching for the key.*

Narrator 2   They searched high.*

Narrator 1   They searched low.*

Narrator 2   They looked over things.*

Narrator 1   They looked under things.*

Narrator 2   Until at last they all spotted the key.*

Narrator 1   And pointed happily to it.*

Narrator 2   They picked it up and locked the door.*

Narrator 1   Then they went upstairs to get ready for bed.*

Narrator 2   But before they did.

Narrator 1   They lit all the candles.*

Narrator 2   They were very careful not to burn themselves.

Narrator 1   Unfortunately they weren't careful enough.

Narrator 2   And they all got their fingers burnt.*

Narrator 1   Which hurt.*

Narrator 2   A lot.*

Narrator 1   And made them wish someone would hurry up and invent electric lights.

Narrator 2   Then the whole family put on their pyjamas.*

Narrator 1   And each got into their own beds.*

Narrator 2   And very soon they all fell asleep.*

Narrator 1   And began to snore.*

Narrator 2   Very loudly.*

Narrator 1   Suddenly, there was a loud knock on the door.*

Narrator 2   Everyone woke up immediately.*

Narrator 1   Rubbed their eyes.*

Narrator 2   Stretched.*

Narrator 1   Yawned.*

Narrator 2   And fell back to sleep.*

Narrator 1   And began snoring again.*

Narrator 2   There was another knock on the door.*

Narrator 1   A very loud knock.*

Narrator 2   A very loud and prolonged knock.*

Narrator 1   The family all woke up.*

Narrator 2   Sat up in their beds.*

Narrator 1   Rubbed their eyes.*

Narrator 2   Stretched.*

Narrator 1   Yawned.*

Narrator 2   And looked at each other.*

Narrator 1   There was another loud knock at the door.*

Narrator 2   Everyone waited for someone else to get up.

Narrator 1   And answer the door.

Narrator 2   But no one did.

Narrator 1   Instead, they all lay back down.*

Narrator 2   Put their pillows over their heads to cut out the noise.*

Narrator 1   And went back to sleep.*

Narrator 2   And began snoring very loudly.*

Narrator 1   There was another knock on the door.*

Narrator 2   Even louder and more prolonged.*

Narrator 1   Than the loud and prolonged knock there had been last time.

Narrator 2   The whole family woke up.*

Narrator 1   Sat up in their beds.*

Narrator 2   Rubbed their eyes.*

Narrator 1   Stretched.*

Narrator 2   Yawned.*

Narrator 1   And slowly got out of bed.*

Narrator 2   They each put on their dressing gowns.*

Narrator 1   And their novelty slippers.*

Narrator 2   In the shape of giant fig rolls.

Narrator 1   And walked over to the window.*

Narrator 2   The whole family opened the window.*

Narrator 1   At least they tried to.

Narrator 2   But it was rather stiff.

Narrator 1   Because it had just been painted.

Narrator 2   They pushed and they pushed.*

Narrator 1   And shoved and struggled.*

Narrator 2   Until at last, the window opened.*

Narrator 1   Very suddenly.

Narrator 2   So that they lost their balance.*

Narrator 1   And just caught it in time to stop themselves toppling head first out of the window.*

Narrator 2   Which would have brought the story to a rather messy end.

Narrator 1   So it's a jolly good job it didn't happen.

Narrator 2   The family peered out of the window.*

Narrator 1   And down below they saw a friend.*

Narrator 2   Who had started knocking on their door again.*

Narrator 1   'Stop it!' the whole family cried.

Narrator 2   So the friend stopped it.

Narrator 1   He looked up at the family.*

Narrator 2   And the family looked down at him.*

Narrator 1   'Don't you know what time it is?' asked the family.

Narrator 2   And they all pointed up at the moon.*

Narrator 1   'Cos they didn't have any clocks or watches.

Narrator 2   'Yes I do,' said the friend.

Narrator 1   And he pointed up at the moon.*

Narrator 2   Just for good measure.

Narrator 1   'But I need your help. Just listen.'

Narrator 2   The whole family got ready to listen.

Narrator 1 Really ready by craning their necks and cupping their hands to their ears.*

Narrator 2 'I have just had some unexpected guests arrive,' said the friend.

Narrator 1 Wringing his hands in agitation.*

Narrator 2 A bit more agitated than that.*

Narrator 1 'And I'm right out of food.'

Narrator 2 'You couldn't lend me a loaf of bread, could you?'

Narrator 1 The whole family stood and scratched their heads in thought.*

Narrator 2 Then they all pointed at the friend.*

Narrator 1 'Don't bother us,' they said.

Narrator 2 'It's the middle of the night!'

Narrator 1 And they all pointed back at the moon, to show they weren't lying.*

Narrator 2 Then they closed the window.*

Narrator 1 Which was rather stiff.

Narrator 2 And got back into their beds.*

Narrator 1 The friend began to knock again.*

Narrator 2 And knock.*

Narrator 1 And knock.*

Narrator 2 The whole family tutted.*

Narrator 1 And got out of bed.*

Narrator 2 And walked back over to the window.*

Narrator 1   Which they opened.*

Narrator 2   With difficulty.*

Narrator 1   What with it having been painted recently.

Narrator 2   And they looked down at the friend.*

Narrator 1   'What do you want?' they said, pointing at him.*

Narrator 2   The friend looked pleadingly at them.

Narrator 1   As pleadingly as he could.*

Narrator 2   'Just a loaf of bread,' he said.

Narrator 1   'Can't I borrow just a loaf of bread?'

Narrator 2   The family looked at each other.*

Narrator 1   Sighed.*

Narrator 2   And then nodded.*

Narrator 1   And off they went to the larder.*

Narrator 2   Between them all, they carried the loaf of bread back to the window.*

Narrator 1   Because it was heavy.

Narrator 2   Very heavy.

Narrator 1   And then they threw it out.*

Narrator 2   The friend caught it.*

Narrator 1   Just.

Narrator 2   And waved back at the family.*

Narrator 1   A very big, 'Thank you', sort of wave.*

Narrator 2   And hurried off to his guests.*

Narrator 1   The family all shut the window.*

Narrator 2   Got back into bed.*

Narrator 1   Got out of bed.*

Narrator 2   Blew out the candles.*

Narrator 1   Got back into bed.*

Narrator 2   And went back to sleep.*

Narrator 1   Thinking to themselves.

Narrator 2   That someone had asked.

Narrator 1   And they had received.

Narrator 2   Even if it had been the middle of the night!

Dinner Is Served

otherwise known as

The Parable of the Great Banquet

Cast   Man (who holds banquet)
Servants
Person with oxen
Person with field
Person just married

* Where this symbol appears in the script, the narrators wait for the appropriate action to be performed.

Narrator 1   There was once a man who decided to hold a great banquet.

Narrator 2   He must have had big hands.

Narrator 1   What?

Narrator 2   He must have had big hands to hold a big banquet.

Narrator 1   *(Explaining)* Not 'hold' in his hands but 'hold'; 'to have' a great banquet.

Narrator 2   I see.

Narrator 1   The man called for his servants to come forth.

Narrator 2   Who came first, second and third then?

Narrator 1   *(Threatening)* I'm warning you.

Narrator 2   Sorry.

Narrator 1   The man called for his servants who all hurried into the room.*

Narrator 2   They bowed graciously to their master and stood ready to listen.*

Narrator 1   Their master explained that he wanted a big banquet prepared.

Narrator 2   So the servants got on with it straight away.

Narrator 1   First of all they covered the huge banqueting table with a table cloth.*

Narrator 2   Then they uncovered the huge banqueting table because the table cloth was rather creased and needed ironing.*

Narrator 1   So they all set about ironing the table cloth.*

Narrator 2   When all the creases were out.

Narrator 1   They covered the huge banqueting table with the table cloth.*

Narrator 2   And then they set out the plates.*

Narrator 1   And the bowls.*

Narrator 2   And the cutlery.*

Narrator 1   Knives.*

Narrator 2   One for fish, one for meat.*

Narrator 1   Forks.*

Narrator 2   And spoons.*

Narrator 1   Last of all they got out the glasses.*

Narrator 2   Which they carefully polished.*

Narrator 1   *(Getting rather carried away)* Very carefully so they glistened and sparkled and glinted like the sun reflecting on the still pools of crystal clear water that idle their way in the green valleys.

Narrator 2 Thank you.

Narrator 1 Which they carefully polished and put on the table.*

Narrator 2 The servants were very pleased with themselves and smiled at each other.*

Narrator 1 Then they went to see their master.

Narrator 2 They bowed.*

Narrator 1 And showed him how beautiful the banqueting table looked.

Narrator 2 He walked up and down looking at what had been prepared.*

Narrator 1 All the time he shook his head from side to side.*

Narrator 2 The servants looked worried.*

Narrator 1 Very worried.*

Narrator 2 Suddenly their master stopped and pointed at them all.*

Narrator 1 He exclaimed that the banqueting table looked wonderful.

Narrator 2 The servants were so happy they gave a cheer.*

Narrator 1 And danced a little dance of joy.*

Narrator 2 Until their master interrupted them.

Narrator 1 To say that whilst the table looked lovely, didn't they think there ought to be some food?

Narrator 2 The servants all looked very embarrassed.*

Narrator 1 Rather ashamed.

Narrator 2 And a bit sheepish.

Narrator 1   Baaa!

Narrator 2   So, straight away the servants began preparing the food.*

Narrator 1   Chickens, from which they had to pluck all the feathers.*

Narrator 2   And then stuff with a mixture of breadcrumbs and exotic herbs.*

Narrator 1   They chopped and peeled onions.*

Narrator 2   Which made them cry.*

Narrator 1   Lots and lots.*

Narrator 2   They beat eggs.*

Narrator 1   Whipped cream.*

Narrator 2   Battered fish.*

Narrator 1   And were rather violent to lots of other food as well.

Narrator 2   It was very hot work.

Narrator 1   But at last all the food was prepared.

Narrator 2   The servants placed it carefully on the huge banqueting table.*

Narrator 1   Their master came in and smelled the food.*

Narrator 2   Very enthusiastically.

Narrator 1   And tasted the food.*

Narrator 2   Very greedily.

Narrator 1   Then he smiled a big smile.*

Narrator 2   His banquet was ready.

Narrator 1   He told the servants to go and fetch all the invited guests.

Narrator 2   So off they went, bowing as they left.*

Narrator 1   When they got to the first guest's house they knocked on the door.*

Narrator 2   There was no reply, so they knocked again.*

Narrator 1   There was still no reply, so they all went round the back.*

Narrator 2   Where they found the guest carefully leading two oxen up and down his back garden.*

Narrator 1   Unfortunately the oxen were rather stubborn and had to be dragged along.*

Narrator 2   The guest saw the servants and waved to them.*

Narrator 1   The servants saw the guest and waved back.*

Narrator 2   And then they stopped waving because they all realised they'd stepped in something nasty the oxen had left behind.*

Narrator 1   So they hurriedly tried to remove it from their shoes.*

Narrator 2   Then they explained to the guest that the banquet was ready and he was expected straight away.

Narrator 1   But the guest said that he couldn't come now that he had his two oxen.

Narrator 2   Because he needed to lead them up and down the garden . . .

Narrator 1   Path.

Narrator 2   A few more times.

Narrator 1	And off he went dragging his stubborn oxen behind him. *
Narrator 2	The servants left and hurried to the house of the next guest. *
Narrator 1	They knocked on the door. *
Narrator 2	And they knocked again. *
Narrator 1	It was opened hurriedly by the guest, who looked a little flustered. *
Narrator 2	He explained that he was rather busy because he'd just bought a field.
Narrator 1	And he needed to keep an eye on the grass.
Narrator 2	Just to make sure it was growing properly and he hadn't been conned.
Narrator 1	So he asked the servants if they could help.
Narrator 2	The servants followed the guest out into the field. *
Narrator 1	And they stood and watched the grass. *
Narrator 2	And they watched. *
Narrator 1	And they watched. *
Narrator 2	And they got very bored.
Narrator 1	Then they remembered why they had come. 'It's time for the banquet. Everything is ready and you are expected,' said the servants.
Narrator 2	'I have other priorities now,' said the man as he stood and watched his grass.
Narrator 1	Sadly, the servants left and knocked on the door of the next guest. *

Narrator 2 Who opened the door and smiled at the servants.*

Narrator 1 Then he invited them in and offered them all a drink.*

Narrator 2 Which they all accepted gratefully.

Narrator 1 'I have just got married,' he explained.

Narrator 2 So the servants proposed a toast to the new bride and groom.*

Narrator 1 Made a few speeches.*

Narrator 2 With a few bad jokes.*

Narrator 1 Read some telegrams.*

Narrator 2 And then did some rather embarrassing dancing.*

Narrator 1 Before each having a slice of cake.*

Narrator 2 Then they said, 'It's time for the banquet. Everything is ready and you are expected.'

Narrator 1 But the groom shook his head.*

Narrator 2 And said, 'I have other priorities now. And besides the wife would kill me.'

Narrator 1 So the servants left, ready to go back to their master.

Narrator 2 They looked sad.*

Narrator 1 And dejected.*

Narrator 2 And upset.*

Narrator 1 So with big frowns, they made their way back.*

Narrator 2 They explained everything to their master.

Narrator 1   Who was so cross that he began to shake.*

Narrator 2   Then all the servants began to shake.*

Narrator 1   Just to show that they knew how their master must be feeling.

Narrator 2   When he had calmed down, their master told the servants that they must go out to the highways and the byways.

Narrator 1   The byways and the highways.

Narrator 2   And invite anybody.

Narrator 1   Anybody at all.

Narrator 2   To come to the banquet.

Narrator 1   So the servants bowed and left to do just that.*

Narrator 2   Whilst the master stood solemnly there.*

Narrator 1   Knowing that even if the invited guests felt they were too busy to come, the banquet would still go ahead.

Narrator 2   Most definitely go ahead.

Narrator 1   Without a shadow of a doubt go ahead.

Narrator 2   Without them!

Shepherd's Story Has Them Flocking

otherwise known as

The Parable of the Lost Sheep

Cast	Shepherd Sheep (a flock of) One lost sheep

* Where this symbol appears in the script, the narrators wait for the appropriate action to be performed.

Narrator 1   There was once a shepherd who had lots of sheep.

Narrator 2   And not fish.

Narrator 1   *(To Narrator 2)* Pardon?

Narrator 2   *(To Narrator 1)* Well if he had lots of fish instead of sheep he would have been a fishmonger and not a shepherd.

Narrator 1   *(To Narrator 2)* I think that's enough from you.

Narrator 2   *(To Narrator 1)* Only trying to help.

Narrator 1   There was once a shepherd who had lots of sheep.

Narrator 2   Lots and lots of sheep.

Narrator 1   In fact he had 100 sheep.

Narrator 2   The shepherd often spent his time carefully counting the sheep.*

Narrator 1   Just to make sure that they were all there.

Narrator 2   And when he wasn't counting the sheep the shepherd was busy doing other shepherdy things.

Narrator 1   Like whittling sticks into interesting shapes.*

Narrator 2   Though he wasn't always as careful as he should be.

Narrator 1   And he sometimes cut his finger.*

Narrator 2   Which hurt.*

Narrator 1   A lot!*

Narrator 2   And when he wasn't whittling, he sometimes practised a bit of juggling.*

Narrator 1   With three heavy rocks.

Narrator 2   He was quite good at juggling, but did have a tendency to drop the rocks.*

Narrator 1   On his foot.*

Narrator 2   Now, whilst the shepherd was busy counting and whittling and juggling.

Narrator 1   The sheep were busy being sheep.

Narrator 2   And doing sheep sort of things.

Narrator 1   The sheep baa-ed a lot.*

Narrator 2   Really very loudly.*

Narrator 1   They ate the grass.*

Narrator 2   Really very hungrily.*

Narrator 1   And they followed each other about.*

Narrator 2   Really very stupidly.

Narrator 1   One evening as the sun began to set.

Narrator 2   The sheep were feeling rather cold.*

Narrator 1   So cold that they began to shiver.*

Narrator 2   Quite a lot.*

Narrator 1   They huddled together to keep warm.*

Narrator 2   What they needed to protect themselves against the cold was something like a warm jumper.

Narrator 1   A warm woolly jumper.

Narrator 2   And then they realised that they'd each got a warm woolly fleece on already.

Narrator 1   So they stopped feeling cold.*

Narrator 2   And smiled big, happy, sheepy smiles.*

Narrator 1   The shepherd.

Narrator 2   Who didn't have a warm, woolly fleece.

Narrator 1   Was feeling cold.

Narrator 2   So he did some running on the spot to keep warm.*

Narrator 1   Some very vigorous running on the spot.*

Narrator 2   Until he was very warm indeed.*

Narrator 1   And then he began to count his sheep again.*

Narrator 2   Not his fish.

Narrator 1   *(Giving Narrator 2 a steely glance)* Just to make sure that he still had 100.

Narrator 2   Carefully he counted.*

Narrator 1   Very carefully.*

Narrator 2   But oh dear!

Narrator 1   Although he'd counted carefully, he'd only counted 99 sheep.

Narrator 2	One was missing!
Narrator 1	The shepherd looked very unhappy.*
Narrator 2	And when the sheep saw how unhappy the shepherd looked, they looked unhappy as well.*
Narrator 1	Very unhappy.*
Narrator 2	The shepherd was so unhappy, that he began to cry.*
Narrator 1	So did the sheep.*
Narrator 2	But then the shepherd stopped.*
Narrator 1	Stood up straight.*
Narrator 2	Very straight.*
Narrator 1	And decided on what he would do.
Narrator 2	He would go and look for the missing sheep.
Narrator 1	He turned to his remaining flock and explained that he was going to look for the missing sheep.*
Narrator 2	The other sheep looked at him admiringly.*
Narrator 1	And began to baa.*
Narrator 2	They were very impressed.
Narrator 1	The shepherd waved to the sheep.*
Narrator 2	The sheep waved back, as only a sheep can.*
Narrator 1	And then he set off.*
Narrator 2	Carefully closing the gate of the fold behind him.*
Narrator 1	To stop any other sheep escaping.

Narrator 2   Which would have defeated the purpose somewhat if they had.

Narrator 1   Since, whilst he was looking for his lost sheep, he would have found that he'd been losing sheep.

Narrator 2   So with the fold securely shut, the shepherd set off.

Narrator 1   He looked to the left.*

Narrator 2   And he looked to the right.*

Narrator 1   He looked up high.*

Narrator 2   And he looked down low.*

Narrator 1   He looked in places where a sheep might be.*

Narrator 2   And he looked in places where a sheep just couldn't be . . . just to make sure.*

Narrator 1   At last, after much looking.

Narrator 2   And searching.

Narrator 1   The shepherd heard a noise in the distance.*

Narrator 2   A noise that made him smile a big, broad smile.*

Narrator 1   It was the sound of his lost sheep.

Narrator 2   Except it wasn't lost, because the shepherd had found it.*

Narrator 1   The shepherd happily led the lost sheep.*

Narrator 2   Who wasn't.

Narrator 1   Back to the fold.

Narrator 2   With great rejoicing.*

Narrator 1   When the other sheep saw the lost sheep.*

Narrator 2 Who wasn't.

Narrator 1 Returning with the shepherd, they began to baa loudly.*

Narrator 2 Very loudly.*

Narrator 1 They were so pleased to see the lost sheep.

Narrator 2 Who wasn't.

Narrator 1 Back home again.

Narrator 2 The shepherd opened the gate of the fold and the sheep who had been lost, but now wasn't because he had been found.*

Narrator 1 Went in to be with the rest of the flock.*

Narrator 2 The whole flock was so happy that they did a little happy sheepy sort of dance.*

Narrator 1 Which the shepherd joined in.*

Narrator 2 What rejoicing there was!

Narrator 1 All for the sheep who was lost.

Narrator 2 But now was found!